270

TALES OF HEAVEN AND EARTH

Georges Berton is a Professor
of History, a journalist and
an author. He is an expert
on Saint Francis of Assisi.

Cover design by Peter Bennett

Bible quotations are taken from
The New English Bible (1970).

ISBN: 1 85103 241 X
© Editions Gallimard, 1993
Managing editor: Jacqueline Vallon
Adviser for UK edition: Rev. David Jarmy
English text © 1996 by Moonlight Publishing Ltd
First published in the United Kingdom 1996
by Moonlight Publishing Ltd, 36 Stratford Road, London W8
Printed in Italy by Editoriale Zanardi

ST FRANCIS, THE MAN WHO SPOKE TO BIRDS

by Georges Berton

Illustrated by François Place

Translated by Clare Best

Moonlight Publishing

To Jean-Romain,
Maxime and Edouard,
who love little birds.

Amongst the olive trees nestled the ruins of a small church.

Gubbio
Perugia *Assisi
Spoleto
*Rome

Damian lived in
the 3rd century.
He was a doctor
who tended the
poor and needy.
People prayed to
him to protect
them from
accidents.

Near Assisi, in Italy, on the road that leads to Spoleto, stood a tiny church dedicated to Saint Damian. The church was so small that in summer it could barely be seen above the waving corn, and it was anyway so green with moss that it seemed as though it had grown out of the landscape.

Although it was falling into ruins, the church sheltered a great treasure – a golden crucifix. The Christ figure on the cross had a beautiful expression. The priest of Saint Damian would pray: "Dear Jesus, see how the wind and

The word church
comes from
a Greek word
meaning house
of the Lord.

5

Francis went to a cave to think and pray. He lived as a hermit, in solitude. Other Christians (such as Mother Julian of Norwich, for example) and also Muslims and Buddhists, have lived as hermits. Some still do.

the snow have reduced your house to ruins! Must it suffer like this?"

A little distance away, in a cave, lived a young man called Francis. Francis had been baptised John, but his mother, Pica Bernardone, came from Provence, in France. Her son reminded her of her home country and so she had called him Francis. The young man would pray for hours at a time, asking God: "What must I do to become holy?"

The word troubadour came from the language of Provence and means 'the person who finds, invents, composes'. By the 12th and 13th centuries, it had come to mean a poet who made up and sang verses.

Until now, Francis Bernardone had revelled in life's pleasures. As the son of a rich cloth merchant, he had wandered from castle to castle, reciting verses and singing ballads. He was what was known in those days as a troubadour. Francis also had ambitions to be a great soldier, but during the war between Assisi and Perugia he was captured and held as a prisoner for a year in Perugia. When he returned to Assisi, his fellow soldiers barely recognised him.

In the early 13th century Italy was prospering. As cities grew, merchants became wealthy. Peter Bernardone, Francis' father, was a wealthy cloth merchant who travelled widely to buy and sell cloth.

God told Francis to rebuild the church.

Suddenly Francis, who had until now always loved feasts and banquets, was happy only in the company of beggars. He gave all his money to the poor, and when his purse was empty, he gave away his hat, his clothes, even his belt. Then he went to his cave and prayed again to God, begging him to tell him what he should do next.

Since God's response was slow in coming, Francis went to the little church of Saint Damian. The elderly priest was busy tending to his bee-hives, and Francis found himself alone in front of the crucifix. Christ's gentle face smiled down at him: "Francis, my house is falling down – make haste and rebuild it!" The young Francis was overjoyed. He rushed down the hill to his parents' home, loaded his horse with the best lengths of cloth he could find in the house, and went and sold it all to the highest bidder. Then he bought the building materials he would need, and returned to Saint Damian.

Francis wanted to follow Jesus' teaching: "If you wish to go the whole way, go, sell your possessions, and give to the poor, and then you will have riches in heaven; and come, follow me." Matthew, chapter 19, verse 21.

Francis had to learn to live in poverty.

In the Middle Ages, bishops presided over a kind of tribunal. Judgments were made on matters concerning the Church.

When Francis' father found out that his son had taken all his cloth, he flew into a violent rage. But Francis was not there to see it. He was happily perched high up on a scaffold, laying stones one on top of another, and positioning the roof tiles on the little church.

But Peter Bernardone was determined to recover what he had lost, and insisted that his son should appear before the Bishop. A crowd gathered in the square to witness the event, and Francis' father waited to see what fate would befall his errant son. Francis was unafraid. The Bishop said: "The cloth you sold was your father's. He worked hard for it, and you must give it back to him."

He dressed in rags and was always singing.

The gardener at the Bishop's palace gave Francis an old cloak. Francis called himself a Knight of Lady Poverty, and drew a large chalk cross on the cloak.

Francis understood that if he was to serve God, he must do so with what he had, nothing more: "Father, I have only this shirt, but I give it to you!" Francis ran naked to the Bishop, who covered him with his own cloak.

The citizens of Assisi soon became used to meeting this young man who wore rags, but who was so happy that just to see him made you forget your worries. They called him Poverello, meaning little poor man.

Francis travelled all over the country, composing poems and hymns to God and the Virgin Mary, and singing them to astonished crowds. And, wherever he went, people gave him money to rebuild Saint Damian.

Francis sang in the rain and in the wind, and he sang in the sunshine. At night he went to sleep on the bare earth, thanking God for the beauty of flowers, and for the wide sky and the birds that fly across it.

In Umbria it was a hard winter. A wolf prowled around Gubbio.

In spring, Umbria was so beautiful that even the poorest beggars thanked God that they had been born there. But in winter the harsh weather made life difficult. A thick shroud of snow covered the ground. Pine forests and mighty stands of holm oak trees dominated the plain like dark fortresses. Cypress trees stood stiffly in the frozen soil, as so many sentries on duty. Only Francis enjoyed the winter. He thanked God for the whiteness of Sister Snow and wrote hymns to Brother Frost, whose crystals sparkled so brightly.

In the Middle Ages, and even up to the 19th century, wolves were common in Europe. In winter they would come close to human settlements in search of food.

In medieval Italy, towns were governed like little republics. They were ruled over by a magistrate or podesta, a word meaning power.

The wolf of Gubbio, living deep in the dense undergrowth, was ravenous. Each night he left his lair and went out hunting. He would slaughter one or two sheep to feed himself, and would then attack dogs, vagrants, even children, for sheer amusement! This wolf was the devil incarnate: he was strong, sly and elusive. The people of Assisi, Gubbio and Spoleto lived in terror. As soon as night fell, citizens barred their doors and peasants huddled around their fires. Parents put their children to bed with promises that they would not be far away. In church, people prayed novenas, asking for God's protection against the wolf. At the town hall, the podesta drew up battle plans and recruited soldiers to hunt down the wolf. But it was no good, the beast evaded every attempt to capture it.

An advisor from the town hall suggested appealing to Francis for help. His response seemed so strange that the

Christians would pray novenas in times of great danger. These prayers, said over nine successive days, asked God or the Virgin Mary or the Saints for help with a particular problem.

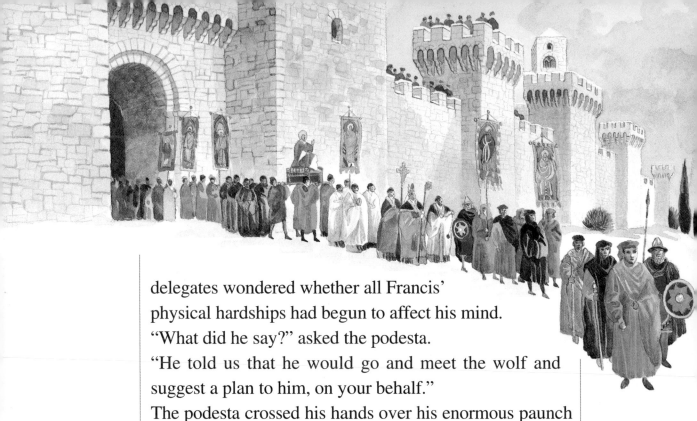

delegates wondered whether all Francis'
physical hardships had begun to affect his mind.

"What did he say?" asked the podesta.

"He told us that he would go and meet the wolf and
suggest a plan to him, on your behalf."

The podesta crossed his hands over his enormous paunch
and pulled a face. It was a sign that he was deep in
thought. Eventually, raising one eyebrow, he said: "Let's
do what Francis asks, and we'll respect any agreement he
makes with the wolf."

It was an extraordinary plan. Francis' idea was to give
the wolf a hearty meal each day, but in return the wolf
must agree to reform his life.

The people gathered at the town gates, as Francis went
out into the snow to meet the wolf. The beast's bright
eyes soon fixed on him, his evil grin exposing vicious
fangs. He could so easily have devoured Francis!

When he was close to the wolf, Francis crouched down

Only Francis dared meet the wolf and make a pact with it.

The legend of the Gubbio wolf brings to mind Isaiah's account of God's kingdom: "The wolf shall live with the sheep, and the leopard lie down with the kid; the calf and the young lion shall grow up together, and a little child shall lead them." (Isaiah, chapter 11, verses 6-9.)

and looked straight into the animal's eyes: "Come to me, my brother, I have something to say to you." The wolf came calmly towards Francis and placed his great paw in the hand held out to him. "Brother Wolf, noble creature of God, you sadden me greatly. Why so much butchery? Does it really give you pleasure to cut throats and break bones?" The wolf answered him: "I do it because I'm hungry, and the smell of blood thrills me." Then Francis said: "These are indeed the snares of the devil! Brother Wolf, if you expel from your heart these evil thoughts of murder and feasting, I promise you a happy life in Gubbio. Each morning the town butcher will make you a tasty meal, and children will come and stroke your silky coat. But first, promise me that you will change your ways."

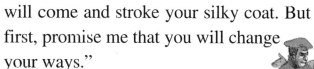

Just at that moment, a glimmer of pink light appeared in the sky and the finest, mild rain began to fall. Spring was on the way. The wolf's fierce expression softened and Francis saw two tears run down his face and drop into the

13

The wolf came to live peacefully in the village.

In the Middle Ages, people were not sentimental about animals as we are in the West today. There were few domesticated animals.

snow. He said: "Come and meet your new friends." The wolf's change of heart was complete. Francis returned to the town with the beast walking as docile as a dog by his side. The townspeople made way for them. With the podesta's agreement, Francis found a place for the wolf to live, between the church and the town square. Brother Wolf led a happy life and enjoyed watching the children at play. As the years passed, he became stiff-legged, slow and blind. When eventually he died, the people of Gubbio mourned his passing, and a huge crowd watched him buried. Francis paid homage to him: "He was a good little monk, poor and humble. He goes before us to heaven."

By his love of animals, Francis wanted to demonstrate the brotherhood that he believed should exist between all God's creatures. Today Francis still inspires people who are concerned about animal rights and environmental issues.

Each morning, Francis marvelled at nature's beauty.

In 1209, three years after his conversion, Francis founded the first community of Brothers in a monastery so small that it was known as Porziuncula, meaning a little bit of a monastery.

When he was staying at the monastery at Porziuncula, Francis would walk in the garden each morning. The cicada would look out for him and, when she heard Francis' call, would perch on his hand. They sang together in the clear morning air: "Thanks be to God, for Brother Wind, for the air and clouds and for the clear skies..." Then the cicada, the tiny troubadour, returned to her cypress tree, whilst Francis wandered slowly on through the garden. He would stop to contemplate the incessant

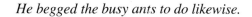

He begged the busy ants to do likewise.

Francis had chosen to live in poverty and own nothing, in order to devote all his time, energy and thoughts to God. That is why he reproaches the ants for thinking only of their subsistence. To admire nature, the work of God, is for Francis the most wonderful of all prayers.

motion of the ants as they ran fom one side of the hedge to the other in a restless black line. "Why are you so agitated?" he would ask them. "Take time to appreciate creation, instead of spending all your days building up stocks of food, always thinking of tomorrow and the day after tomorrow!" Rather like the ants, the gardener at Porziuncula was forever worried about whether or not he grew the best vegetables. His lettuces, his cabbages, his beans – the most tender in the region – were his pride and joy. Thanks to him, the aromas from the cooking pots in the monastery kitchen would have delighted the palate of the most discerning gourmet, prince or cardinal. But the gardener never worried about roses, lilies, or jasmine. Francis remarked to him: "Brother

Christ taught that people should not become too atttached to money or material things, as that can prevent their being receptive to God, and to other people.

Gardener, we are thankful to you for such good food. But you should grow some flowers as well. They would give us their heady scent in the warmth of the evening and our Sisters could decorate the altar with them." Obediently, the gardener set about reducing the area of his kitchen garden. From high in her tree, Sister Cicada would soon look down on roses, petunias, buttercups... Bees would gorge themselves on pollen, and buzz with pleasure as they thanked God for Brother Francis' finer feelings.

Not far away, at Bevagno, the curate was concerned. His parishioners bickered constantly about money. He asked Francis to come and preach in his church, hoping to see joy and peace restored.

Francis suggested that Brother Angelo and Brother Masseo should go with him to Bevagno. They set out early, Francis walking in front and his companions following. Suddenly, Francis stopped: "Look! Our gentle, little lark has come to meet us, and wish us well for our journey."

In the hedgerow by the road, barely visible to any but Francis' keen eye, a grey lark followed their progress. The grey feathers on the bird's neck and back formed the

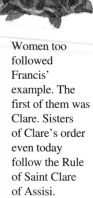

Women too followed Francis' example. The first of them was Clare. Sisters of Clare's order even today follow the Rule of Saint Clare of Assisi.

Francis uses similar words to Christ's in the Gospel: "Look at the birds of the air; they do not sow and reap and store in barns, yet your heavenly Father feeds them. You are worth more than the birds! ... Set your mind on God's kingdom and his justice before everything else, and all the rest will come to you as well. So do not be anxious about tomorrow; tomorrow will look after itself. Each day has troubles enough of its own." (Matthew, chapter 6, verses 26-34)

shape of a hooded cloak. "With her hood," explained Francis, "Sister Lark looks like us, and with her dun-coloured feathers, she shows us how to be content with poor, coarse clothing. Soaring high on the breeze, she teaches us to leave behind us the things of this world and prepare here below for our home in Heaven."

The sun beat down on the travellers as they arrived at Pian d'Area. There were several copses of holm oaks there, and a beech tree and, just by the road, a walnut tree in full leaf that gave plenty of shade. "Rest here, and wait for me," Francis told Angelo and Masseo, "I'm going to preach to the birds." As he approached the beech tree a crowd of birds assembled there to hear him – there were bullfinches and chaffinches, blackbirds, bluetits and sparrows... Francis asked them all to perch on the branches of the holm oak trees and be quiet while he spoke. And they did as he said, like obedient schoolchildren.

Birds, because they fly, seem to be part of a heavenly world. They are sometimes thought of as messengers between heaven and earth.

"Little Brothers," said Francis, "You must give thanks to God! He has given you the freedom of flight, handsome plumage and plenty of food to eat. He has taught you beautiful songs. He has given you azure skies, and silver rivers, and dew. Give Him thanks!" The tiny creatures listened to Francis in total silence. When he had finished speaking, Francis sent them on their way: "Go now! Go and fly, and sing!"

Brother Angelo and Brother Masseo were just waking up when they saw a great cross spreading out above them: it was formed by the birds flying to the four corners of the sky, in full song, just as Francis had told them to.

The next day, Brother Angelo went up into the pulpit and spoke of cicadas and bees, of salads making way for roses, of the lark and of the ants. And everyone thought: "Perhaps we should be a little more like the cicada, and we should forget this world and dream of the heavens where the lark sings as he soars..."

In some Christian churches, priests hear confessions. Believers enter a confessional box and admit their sins. A priest listens, unseen, the other side of a curtain. He can give absolution, or forgiveness.

Francis and Paul walked together, *and talked.*

In a few years, the family of Brothers and Sisters of Francis grew quite large. Each member of the family was obedient to the Rule of Francis, approved by the Pope, Honorius III, in 1223. Franciscans still follow the same Rule today.

Francis was particularly fond of Brother Paul, who was an intelligent man, gentle when caring for the weak, strong in standing up to wickedness. Francis made Paul his minister in the province of Ancona, where there were many Franciscan monasteries. One day, Paul and Francis set out to visit one of two monasteries in the little town of Osimo. On the way there, they talked of all kinds of things: wars, violence and poverty, but also gentleness,

This was the time of the Crusades. In Palestine, the homeland of Jesus, Muslims and Christians fought each other. Christian Crusaders claimed ownership of the Holy Land and set out from Europe to take it back from the Muslims who lived there.

21

In Matthew's Gospel, Jesus' arrest is told thus: "Judas, one of the Twelve, appeared; with him was a great crowd armed with swords and cudgels... They came forward and seized Jesus".

compassion, the devotion of Jesus' followers. On their walk, they cut across a field where they met a herdsman with his goats. The goats were ill-tempered, naughty and skittish, jumping about all over the place, and it was all the herdsman could do to lead them along the path, shouting at them and beating them with his stick.

Francis noticed a lamb in the middle of the herd: it was gentle and obedient and came quietly towards him, stopping occasionally to graze. It was not at all worried by the scatterbrained female goats who jostled it, nor by the billy-goats who ran into it. Francis, taking pity on the lamb, cried out: "Brother Paul, see this lamb that is lost among the goats. It was surely like this that Jesus Christ went meekly among the soldiers who

Goats represent whim, wilfulness, agitation. The lamb, on the other hand, stands for gentleness, humility and patience, the virtues that are most important to Francis.

Francis felt sorry for the one lamb among the goats.

The Order founded by Francis, the Friars Minor, came also to be known as the Mendicant Friars. They renounced ownership of money and all possessions and depended on the gifts of others in order to live.

led him to his torment? We'll go and buy this lamb and take it with us." But Paul asked Francis: "How can we pay for it? We have only our sandals and tunics to offer in exchange; the herdsman will never accept them."

The two Brothers sat down beside the road and wept and wept for the fate of the lamb. A passing merchant was moved to see their sorrow. He was a good man, a man who was constantly thanking God for his good fortune and who always gave part of his earnings to the monastery to be distributed as alms among the poor. Without a moment's hesitation, the merchant gave Francis a purse of money.

In many religions, people are asked to give charity, or alms, to help the poor. It is often priests or monks who are given the responsibility of distributing this money. The word alms comes from a Greek word meaning compassion.

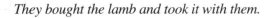

Francis and Paul were overjoyed and went to find the herdsman, who was actually glad to exchange the lamb for a purse of money. And so they carried on towards Osimo, the lamb walking between the two men.

"How are we going to look after it?" asked Francis. "We live a life of poverty, we have nothing to give it."

"Let us entrust it to the Servants of Christ at Saint Severino," replied Paul. "They are good, holy women and they can do a lot of things that we can't."

Francis thanked God for Paul's intelligence.

When Francis and Paul arrived at Saint Severino, the Sisters gathered in the cloister, full of joy and laughter to see the little lamb grazing there. They fed the lamb well and cared for it, treating it as a gift from God.

The lamb lived with them for some years at the convent, and grew to be a fine sheep.

When the right season came, the Sisters sheared the creature's wool, spun it, and wove it into a new habit for Francis, to replace his old, threadbare cowl.

Francis and his companions wore a rough tunic or habit like the peasants of the time. It had a hood to give protection against the weather. The garment was known as a frock, or cowl. A priest who is asked to leave his ministry is still sometimes said to be 'defrocked'.

At the monastery of Porziuncula, Brother Morico followed Francis' rule to the letter. He never cheated. In the spirit of penitence, Christians were required to abstain from eating meat each Friday – this was called fasting. It was a rule Morico would never break.

But what if the great religious festival of Christmas fell on a Friday – was it really necessary to give up stew and make do with eggs or fish? There was a doubt in Brother Morico's mind. He mentioned it to Francis, whose response was: "What do you mean? It would be a sin to

Friday is traditionally a fast day for Christians, because Christ died on a Friday.

The practice of fasting is common to many religions. To fast means to refrain from eating or drinking for several hours or days at a time. Fasting is thought to cleanse and purify thc body and soul, and to bring humility. Nowadays, among Christians, fasting usually means giving up just meat.

"Oh no," replied Francis, "always feast at Christmas!"

According to tradition, Jesus was born in Bethlehem, in Judaea, as was his ancestor King David.

Morico's habit is made of a kind of horsehair, often used for stuffing mattresses. When woven, it makes a rough, strong material.

think of Jesus' birthday as like a Friday! The day that God came to earth as a little baby, on that day especially everyone should rejoice and eat meat! Brother Morico, which animals kept Jesus warm in that stable in Bethlehem?"

"Everyone knows that, Francis – the ox and the donkey."

"So," said Francis, "for that reason, on Christmas Day, donkeys and oxen deserve to have a double ration of hay and oats."

Brother Morico made his way to the chapel, lost in thought, his arms folded and his hands buried deep in the warmth of his rough woollen habit. Before long Francis followed him there, and they knelt together in front of the Virgin Mary and recited the Angelus prayer: 'The Son of God has come to live among us. Hail, Mary, full of grace. Blessed art thou among women and blessed is the fruit of thy womb, Jesus.'

When the two men went to join the other Brothers in the refectory, Morico noticed tears running down Francis' cheeks into his beard. It was something that happened quite often

It was Origen, a Christian scholar of the 3rd century, who introduced to the Christmas story the idea of the ox and the donkey in the stable in Bethlehem.

The Angelus is a prayer dedicated to Mary, the mother of Jesus Christ. The Angelus is traditionally said three times a day – at dawn, at midday and at dusk.

In early December, Francis had a new idea for Christmas.

these days, especially when Francis meditated on the baby in the manger in Bethlehem.

In the neighbouring village of Greccio lived a friend of the Brothers, called John Vellita. He was a wealthy man, an old soldier, but he lived humbly like a religious Brother, for the love of Christ. At the beginning of December, Francis went to visit him.

"John," said Francis, "in a few weeks Christmas will be here. It is time to prepare for the great feast."

For Christians, the four weeks leading up to Christmas are a period of waiting, and of preparation for the feast. This period is called Advent, from the Latin word meaning 'approach'.

Christmas, 25th December, is one of the great Christian feasts. On this day Christians celebrate Christ's birth. The date corresponds to the winter solstice, darkest mid-winter. Before there was a Christian feast, there was a festival of light, to celebrate the sun regaining strength after winter. The pagan feast was taken into the Christian calendar in the 4th century, since Christians believe Christ came into the world as God's light.

It was to re-enact the birth of Jesus at Bethlehem.

It was Francis' idea to make the first crib, for Christmas 1223. Ever since then, all over the world – in Provence, in Spain, in Bavaria, in Mexico – sculptors and clay modellers have followed the tradition.

John replied: "Yes, yes, Brother Francis, but I fail to see how I can be of service to you." "Listen to me," said Francis, "and you will soon understand."

John Vellita owned a stretch of steep, rocky hillside, opposite the valley of Spoleto. "I would like to gather the faithful together in one of the caves," said Francis, "and make a crib just like the one at Bethlehem."

Vellita frowned. Francis was eager to reassure him: "Don't worry! I have permission from the Pope."

From Assisi, from villages and farms all down the valley, a procession came together. Merchants, peasants and craftsmen all joined in a joyous pilgrimage to the grotto. Children romped through the snow, dogs yapping at their heels, and everybody sang in chorus: "Come, midnight has sounded. It's time to set out, the baby Jesus is born."

In the grotto, the Brothers and Sisters of Penitence from the convent of Sister Clare had created something wonderful: on straw spread out on the ground lay a baby, watched over by a Sister and by Brother

Provence, the part of southern France where Francis' mother came from, is famous for its cribs. Clay modellers make santons, meaning saints in the language of Provence. There are figures representing all the characters of the Christmas story, as well as figures of ordinary people from daily life.

That is how the first crib came to be made.

Morico, who played the role of Saint Joseph. An ox lent by a local farmer, and a grey donkey, kept the infant warm with their breath. An altar had been made on an overhanging ledge of rock. The Brothers and Sisters sang the Christmas service and the crowd responded: "Amen! Alleluia!"

In a dark corner of the cave, several grey larks helped prepare the mass. But how had they known to come? Perhaps one of them overheard a conversation between Francis and his friend Vellita...

Three years passed. At Porziuncula, Brothers and Sisters rejoiced in the splendour of autumn, but they were sad to see Francis become weak, deaf and almost blind so that he could scarcely any longer admire the colour of the leaves or enjoy the birdsong.

The time had come for the Poverello to be reunited with his God. Stretched out on the ground, he struggled to sing the last verse of his Canticle: "Praised be my Lord for our Sister the Death of the body, from which no man can escape."

And despite their sadness, the Sisters and

Francis and the Brothers were not priests. They did not say mass. Instead, like the first deacons of the Christian church, they concentrated on a ministry of preaching.

A few years later, Francis died singing, as he had lived.

The Christmas of the Greccio crib was one of the last of Francis' life. He died three years later, on 3 October 1226.

Brothers in their turn sang the refrain: "Praise ye and bless the Lord, and give thanks unto him, and serve him with great humility."

As evening fell, a deep silence descended on the room where Francis lay, quite still. He had died singing.

A multitude of larks swooped down onto the roof of the little building. They were all grey, as though wearing mourning, and they sang in long, plaintive notes. Then they rose as one bird and flew up into the sky.

The soul of their brother Francis was already in Paradise.

Christians believe that there is another life after death. They believe that we live forever, in Paradise. This word comes from a Greek word meaning garden. It conjures up a place of delight, where goodness prevails. Jesus Christ referred to it as the Kingdom of God.

Francis and the Fioretti

Francis was canonised, or made a saint, by Pope Gregory IX in 1229. Saints can be models for believers to look up to.

Francis sends Sylvester to chase demons from Arezzo.

Francis in a state of ecstasy, at one with God.

After Francis' death, the Friars Minor, who had chosen to live following Francis' Rule, decided to spread the news of Francis' inspiring life and good works.

A blend of history and legend

Francis was a poet. His followers, in their turn, told beautiful stories, without worrying too much about historical accuracy. They strayed into the realm of legend so that the message they wanted to convey would be clear and easy for people to understand. The characters in the tales were people, animals, flowers, all of nature – "all of creation" as Francis himself had put it. The stories of Francis were as fresh and colourful as a bunch of flowers, so they became known as the Fioretti, meaning little flowers in Italian.

Who wrote the Fioretti?

It was not until some years after Francis' death that accurate accounts of his life were written by Thomas de Celano and Bonaventure. The Fioretti are a collection of life-like anecdotes about Francis and his companions. The stories as we know them today came down to us from a 14th-century translation of a Latin text by several authors. These writers knew Francis' companions, and recorded their accounts.

Francis' simplicity

The sincerity and the freedom of Francis' personality are appealing. He is led by his love of God and of all living things. His aim is to rediscover the simple message of Christ told in the Gospel, and to live in brotherhood and joy, in harmony with all nature.

Top, centre: Francis receives stigmata, marks like the wounds of Christ. The marks were thought to be a sign of great holiness.

Centre: portrait of Francis, 1228.

Francis makes a spring gush water to quench the thirst of a peasant.

Francis gives his coat to a poor knight.

All these pictures are taken from frescoes painted by Giotto, 1295-1300.

What is Christianity?

The founder of Christianity

Christianity began about 2,000 years ago with a man called Jesus Christ. He spent his youth in Nazareth. When he was about thirty years old he travelled around Palestine, with his disciples, preaching the coming of God's Kingdom. Crowds of people followed him and listened to him. He was regarded as a very important prophet. He called himself the Son of God, and said that he had been sent by God to live among men.

Palestine at the time of Jesus

Palestine was then a colony of the Roman Empire, reigned over by Augustus. Palestine itself was governed by King Herod, an ally of Rome, but a cruel king whom the Jews despised.

Most of the people of Palestine were Jews, who believed in one God, as revealed to Moses. Their faith was expressed in the fifty holy books that make up the Old Testament of the Bible, written between the 10th and the first century before Christ (BC). The Jewish religion was represented by a clergy consisting of a High Priest, Chief Priests, and many priests and levites, of whom some worked only at the Temple. The Temple of Jerusalem was at the heart of Jewish religious life. With its white stone decorated with gold slabs, surrounded by porticos and columns of marble, it dominated the city. Each morning and evening sacrifices were offered there. When Jesus dared to contest such practices, there was outrage.

The Nativity, or birth, of Christ in a stable. This scene is shown over and over again in paintings.

Men and women who followed Jesus were his disciples. Jesus chose his twelve apostles from among them: Simon Peter, James and John the sons of Zebedee, Andrew, Matthew, Bartholomew, Thaddeus, James the son of Alpheus, Thomas, Simon Zealot, Philip and Judas.

Jesus' fate

The crowds who had followed Jesus began to disperse. He did not seem to be the Messiah they had waited for; they wanted someone to free them from Roman domination and re-establish Palestine as a peaceful kingdom, just as the prophets of the Bible had promised.

To the Jewish clergy, whose job it was to uphold Jewish law, Jesus was a problem because he turned their traditions upside down.

The Romans regarded Jesus as a rebel who could be dangerous. They sentenced him to death and crucified him, at the age of thirty-three. Christians believe that Jesus was resurrected three days after his death. The event is celebrated by Christians at Easter. Christians also believe that Jesus is the Son of God, that he was at once human and divine, that he was the Messiah sent by God to spread a message of peace, love and justice.

The Gospels

Jesus died in about the year AD 30. There was no written record of his teachings, though his existence was documented by Jewish and Roman writers of the 1st and 2nd centuries – Josephus, Tacitus, Pliny.

Jesus' message is set out in the Gospel, a word meaning good news. The Gospel consist of texts written about Jesus by the early Christians. The Church approved the gospels of Matthew, Mark, Luke and John, all of which were written between AD 60 and 95. The first three gospels, Matthew, Mark and Luke, present certain incidents in parallel, and are known as the synoptic gospels.

The first images of Christ showed him as a good shepherd. The picture shown at the top of the page was painted in a catacomb in the 3rd century.

The fish is one of the symbols of Jesus Christ. The letters that form the word fish in Greek are also the initial letters of Jesus Christ, Son of God, Saviour.

Saint John, shown with his symbol, the eagle. The bird dictates John's gospel by divine inspiration, shown as the hand at the top right of the picture. (From a medieval manuscript.)

Francis in history

In 1098, the Cistercian Order was founded. It was an attempt to return to first principles, to the simplicity of the Gospel message. It was a reaction against the excesses of monastic life and the power of monasteries like Cluny. Cistercian monasteries quickly spread across Europe, there were 750 by the late 1200s. The monks combined prayer with manual labour, farming and craft work.

A new world

Francis lived from the late 12th to the early 13th century. It was the most prosperous era of the Middle Ages. In Europe, the population grew rapidly. Towns developed into cities, new towns sprang up near markets, monasteries and castles. The middle classes, made up of rich merchants and skilled craftsmen, sought freedom from their old feudal masters. Universities were founded.

The high point of Christianity

Before he died, Jesus asked his disciples to spread the gospel throughout the whole world. Twelve hundred years later, the church had become a well-organised, extremely wealthy and powerful institution.

Rich monasteries and cathedrals

Europe was made up of a number of countries governed by sovereigns, each of whom claimed a divine right to rule. It was a world united in its Christian culture. The powerful monasteries were often prosperous enough to function as towns in their own right. They had fine libraries and were governed by abbots who lived like kings. They became

1042: Edward the Confessor, King of England.
1066: Battle of Hastings.

1099: Capture of Jerusalem by Crusaders.

1100: Foundation of Order of Knights Templar.

1146: Bernard of Clairvaux preaches the second crusade. Famine in Europe.

1170: Thomas a Becket murdered in Canterbury.

1187: Fall of Jerusalem.

1192: Rebuilding of Lincoln Cathedral.
1199: Death of Richard I.

1200: 530 Cistercian monasteries.
1203: War between Assisi and Perugia.
1204: Crusaders take Constantinople.

In 1216, Saint Dominic created the Dominican Order. He shared with Francis the ideal of poverty. Both orders are sometimes known as mendicant, or begging, orders.

centres of culture and learning. Beautiful and imposing cathedrals were built as witnesses to Christianity throughout Europe. Meanwhile, to the east, Europe fought crusade after crusade against Islam. The main aim of these wars was to reclaim from the Muslims the holy places of Jerusalem, the places central to the life of Christ.

A return to poverty

In many parts of Europe, people wanted to reform the Christian way of life. Some Christians thought the Church had betrayed the teachings of its founder, who had been a poor man in the service of poor people. Some believers formed small sects and rebelled against the Papacy, choosing a simple life with pure ideals, like the Cathars. Such people were persecuted as heretics, hunted down and killed. In 1232, Pope Gregory IX set up an Inquisition to look into and combat the heresies, or wrong beliefs, and to seek out those who had deviated from the teaching of the established Church.

Francis of Assisi was keen to avoid divisions and hatred among Christians. He chose the way of obedience and humility. The order of Friars Minor, which he created, gave new life to the Church of his time.

At the beginning of the 12th century, more and more people were living in cities. The mendicant orders chose to spread the gospel among city dwellers. (Above, centre: medieval city from a 14th-century fresco by Lorenzetti.)

Catholics

Orthodox Christians

Muslims

Pagans

Areas of Orthodox mission

● Place of pilgrimage

† Monastery or cathedral

Christianity in the 13th century

1206: The highest minaret in the world built at Delhi in India.

1209: Order of Friars Minor founded.
1210: Friars Minor approved, Pope Innocent III.
1215: Fourth Lateran Council ruled against heretics.

1216: Dominican Order founded.
1223: Rule of the Friars Minor accepted by Pope Honorius III.

1226: Francis wrote his Canticle.
1227: Francis died. Gengis Khan's empire divided between his sons.

1258: Completion of Salisbury Cathedral.
1265: Simon de Montfort's Model Parliament.

1260 : Consecration of Chartres cathedral.

Top of page: Pope Innocent III approves the Rule of the new community of Friars Minor. (After a fresco by Giotto.)

The Friars Minor

The Friars Minor, also known as Franciscans, now number many thousands all over the world.

Like all monks, they stay single, so that they can devote themselves more fully to prayer and to helping the poor. Some are teachers, others look after the sick. There are some who are missionaries far from home, whilst other monks stay in their own country.

All Franciscans follow Francis' will: to spread the gospel in humility and poverty. Francis told them not to own anything except what was strictly necessary. Public generosity would have to provide for all their other needs.

The Poor Clares

The Poor Clares devote their lives to prayer and live an enclosed life in a convent. They spend much of the day in silence. The sisters do not preach or go out and care for the sick, but they feel united with the world through prayer.

Franciscan communities have taken root in all corners of the world. On the right a Franciscan in Togo preaches the catechism. There are Franciscan brothers in the Church of England.

The Poor Clares take their name from Clare, a companion of Francis. Clare was born in 1194, into a noble family of Assisi. She decided in 1212 to follow Francis' teaching, and lived with a few Sisters in a convent near Saint Damian. After Francis died, Clare wrote her own Rule for the Sisters to live by. She died on 11 August 1253.

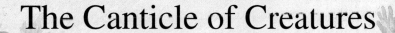

The Canticle of Creatures

Praised be my Lord God
with all his creatures, and especially
our Brother the Sun, who brings us the day
and who brings us the light; fair is he
and shines with a very great splendour.
Praised be my Lord for our Sister the Moon,
and for the stars, which he has
set clear and lovely in heaven.
Praised be my Lord for our brother the Wind,
and for air and cloud, calms and all weather,
by which thou upholdest life in all creatures.
Praised be my Lord for our Sister Water,
who is very serviceable unto us and humble and precious and clean.
Praised be my Lord for our Brother Fire, through whom
thou givest us light in the darkness; and he is bright
and pleasant and very mighty and strong.
Praised be my Lord for our Mother the Earth,
the which doth sustain us and keep us, and bringeth forth
divers fruits, and flowers of many colours, and grass.
Praised be my Lord for all those who pardon one another
for his love's sake, and who endure weakness
and tribulation; blessed are they who peacably
shall endure, for thou, O Most Highest,
shall give them a crown.
Praised be my Lord for our Sister the Death
of the body, from which no man escapeth...
Praise ye and bless the Lord, and give thanks unto him,
and serve him with great humility.

This beautiful poem was written by Francis in 1225, a year before his death. It was written in the dialect of Umbria, where Francis lived. It is one of the first great texts in the Italian language.

Look out for other titles in this series:

SARAH, WHO LOVED LAUGHING
A TALE FROM THE BIBLE

THE SECRETS OF KAIDARA
AN ANIMIST TALE FROM AFRICA

I WANT TO TALK TO GOD
A TALE FROM ISLAM

THE RIVER GODDESS
A TALE FROM HINDUISM

CHILDREN OF THE MOON
YANOMAMI LEGENDS

I'LL TELL YOU A STORY
TALES FROM JUDAISM

THE PRINCE WHO BECAME A BEGGAR
A BUDDHIST TALE

JESUS SAT DOWN AND SAID...
THE PARABLES OF JESUS

MUHAMMAD'S NIGHT JOURNEY
A TALE FROM ISLAM

THE MAGIC OF CHRISTMAS
CHRISTMAS TALES FROM EUROPE